STAR WARS

CONTAINS
STAR WARS
RETURN OF THE
JEDI
CHARACTERS
& VEHICLES

OFFICIAL ANNUAL 2024

Luke Skywalker

Role: Jedi Knight

Skills: Talented pilot, duelist and user of the Force

Equipment: A lightsaber of his own making

Vehicle: An old and trusted T-65 X-wing starfighter (which he flies on a daily basis)

Luke may have been only a farmboy who had newly joined the rebels, but he needed just one shot to destroy the Galactic Empire's huge Death Star battle station.

The Force was strong in Luke, and Obi-Wan Kenobi and Yoda helped him learn how to use it. Even at the age of just 19, he was already a promising Jedi.

To help restore peace to the galaxy, Luke had to face the dreaded Darth Vader. It was during this heated battle that Luke learned Vader was actually his father!

Han Solo has been frozen in carbonite! Find the real Han by looking for the one that matches the bigger image on the left.

What does Luke offer to Jabba the Hutt in exchange for Han's return? Find the right path below and follow it to find out.

BOY, DO I HAVE A SURPRISE FOR YOU!

Who do Luke and his friends disguise themselves as when entering Jabba's palace? Figure out who the heroes are and write their numbers in the spaces below.

A
B
C

A mysterious, disguised figure has come to save Han Solo. Match one puzzle piece to the empty space to find out who it is.

Use the coloured dots as your guide to colour in the picture and discover who has entered Jabba's palace.

A LITTLE HELP HERE?

Which one of these skills does Luke plan to use on Bib Fortuna, so that he can get a meeting with Jabba? Work out which cloud shape matches Luke's and write the letter in the empty space.

A Levitation

B Overconfidence

C Lightsaber

D Mind trick

How was Luke feeling when he said these things?
Draw his expression for each one.

THOSE ARE CUTE EWOKS!

UH-OH! NOT A RANCOR!

I CAN'T BELIEVE HE'S MY FATHER!

Oh, no! Luke is trapped in the rancor pit! Find the character with no matching pair to work out who the rancor eats first.

What does Luke use to stop the mighty rancor from devouring him?
Work out which piece belongs with the picture to find out.

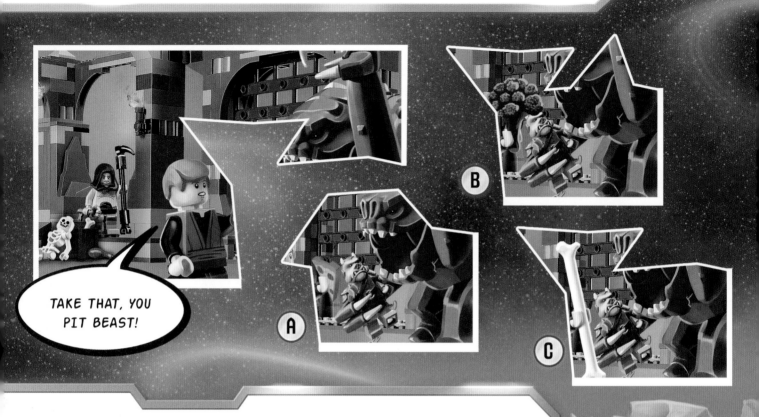

Help Luke escape by finding a route to the exit that avoids the
hungry rancors.

Four of the picture pieces below are taken from the main image of Jabba's sail barge. Can you spot which ones they are?

1

2

3

4

5

IF I WERE A HERO ...

PLANET TATOOINE, IN THE GALAXY'S OUTER RIM. C-3PO AND LUKE SKYWALKER ARE SEARCHING THE DESERT FOR R2-D2, A FEISTY DROID THAT HAS ESCAPED FROM LUKE'S UNCLE'S MOISTURE FARM ...

I'M SURE WE'LL FIND HIM QUICKLY, MASTER LUKE.

DON'T CALL ME MASTER, THREEPIO. I'M JUST A FARMER.

I WISH I WERE A HERO, THOUGH. I COULD GO ON ALL KINDS OF HEROIC MISSIONS!

I COULD RESCUE A PRINCESS!

DO I LOOK LIKE I NEED TO BE RESCUED?

Put this desert skiff back together by writing the number for each part in the right place.

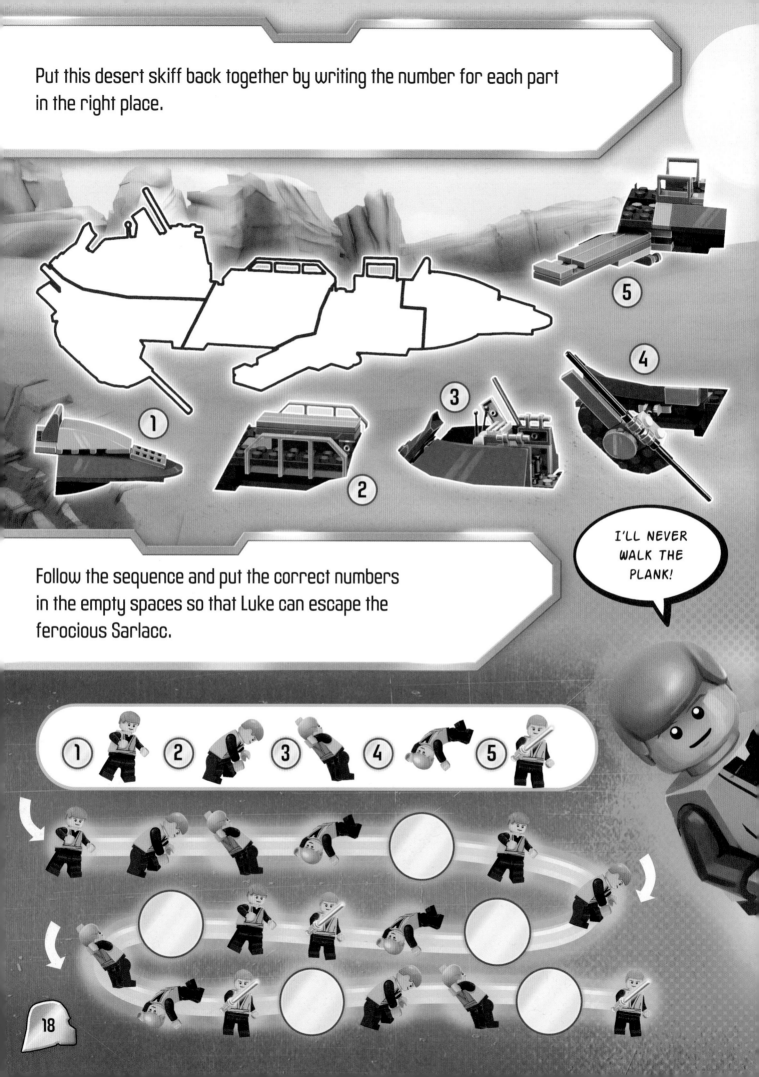

Follow the sequence and put the correct numbers in the empty spaces so that Luke can escape the ferocious Sarlacc.

I'LL NEVER WALK THE PLANK!

Take a look at this gallery of Jabba and his henchmen. Once you've studied it for two minutes, turn the page for a memory test.

Can you remember where each villain was in the gallery on the previous page? Try to write their numbers in the spaces without looking back.

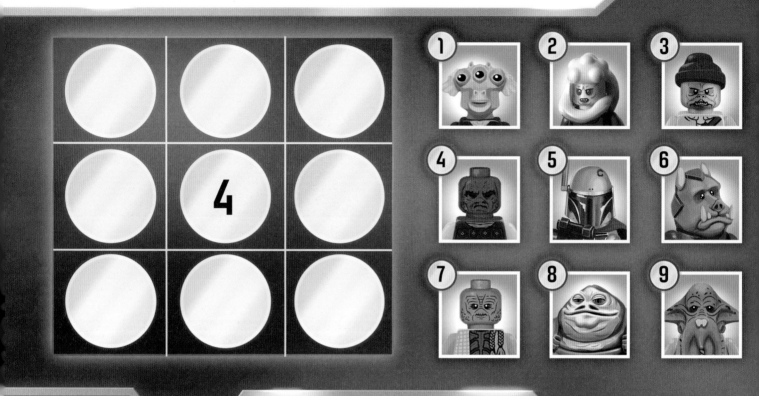

Look at the four possible paths on the right-hand side.
Which one should Luke choose so he can battle as many
of Jabba's henchmen as possible?

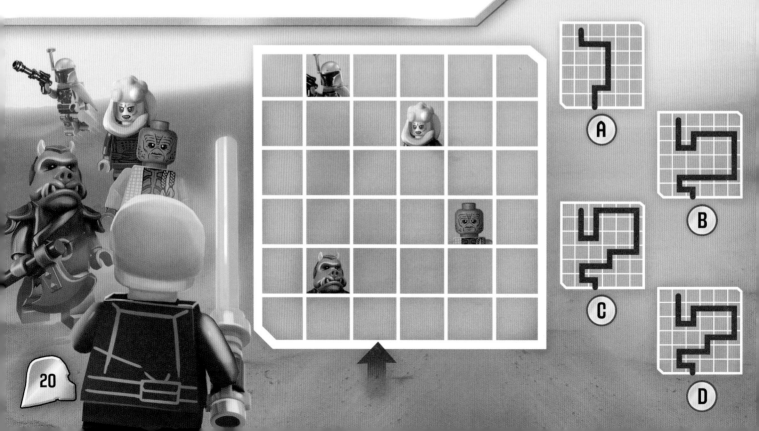

Fill in the empty spaces with the right numbers or draw in the pictures, so that every ship appears just once in each row and column.

Match the silhouettes to find out who sits behind the controls of each of the space vehicles above.

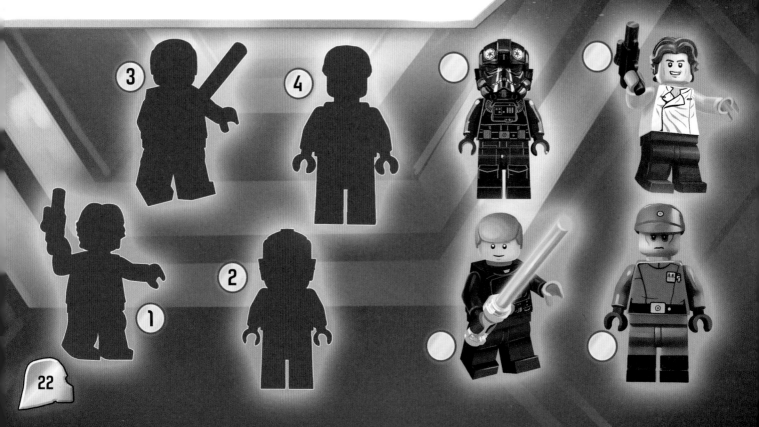

Who is the wise friend that Luke seeks in the Dagobah system?
Find the path of arrows that matches the path in the box to find out.

SOME PATHS CAN BE DANGEROUS.

23

Yoda has told Luke that he must confront someone before he can become a Jedi. Follow the colour code in the order shown to find out who it is.

START

COLOUR CODE

Connect the matching circles. The character who is not crossed by a straight line is another Skywalker. One line has been added for you.

24

Find the character combinations below on the grid. The character left over at the end visits Luke as a Force ghost. One combination has been found for you.

Admiral Ackbar is the commander of the Rebel Alliance starfleet. Use the grid to finish this picture of him.

MAY THE FORCE BE WITH YOU!

Darth Vader can feel someone's presence approaching the Forest Moon of Endor. Match the code to the character to find out who it is.

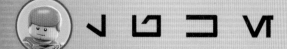

Work out where the missing pieces belong on the stolen Imperial Shuttle *Tydirium*, and write their numbers in the empty spaces.

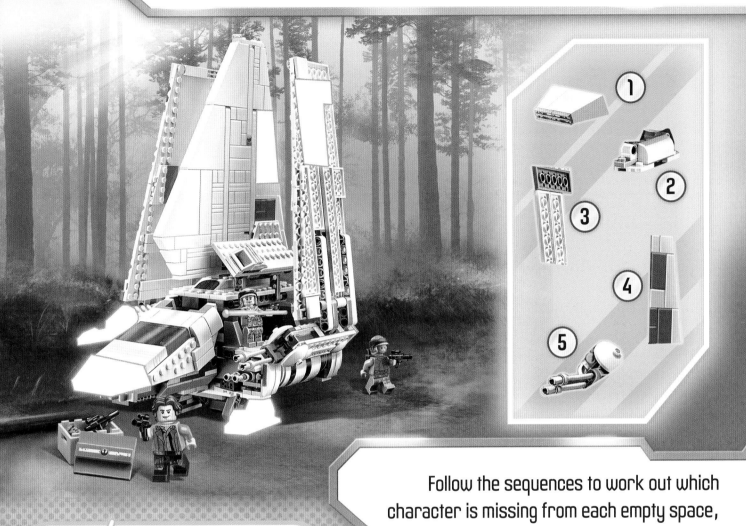

Follow the sequences to work out which character is missing from each empty space, and write their numbers in the circles.

Use the clues below to help Lando Calrissian and Nien Nunb find the way to the second Death Star. They can only move horizontally or vertically on the grid.

START

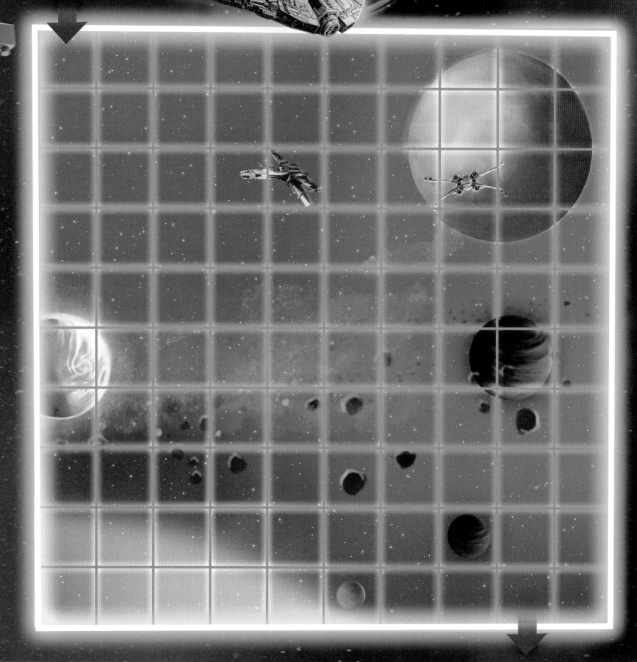

FINISH

28

The rebels dress in camouflage to hide in Endor's forest. They blend in so well that Luke can hardly see his friends! Can you find Chewbacca, Leia and Han?

Oh, no! Scout troopers! Can you number these platoons of scout troopers from 1 to 4, in order of fewest to most?

ONE SCOUT TROOPER IS ONE TOO MANY!

Leia and Luke have jumped on a speeder bike to chase the scout troopers! Can you find which speeder bike matches theirs?

A

B

C

D

E

Luke has jumped across to his own speeder bike. Write numbers above the second picture to put the jumbled pieces back in order.

1	2	3	4	5

Help Luke find a route through the Endor forest that avoids the scout troopers.

Finding someone in this galactic crowd is not an easy task! Take on the challenge by matching the identical characters in neighbouring groups. The first pair has been found for you.

Connect the dots to find out who helped Luke to chase off the scout troopers.

The scout troopers have opened fire! Look at the path options below and choose the one that will allow Luke to defeat the most scout troopers.

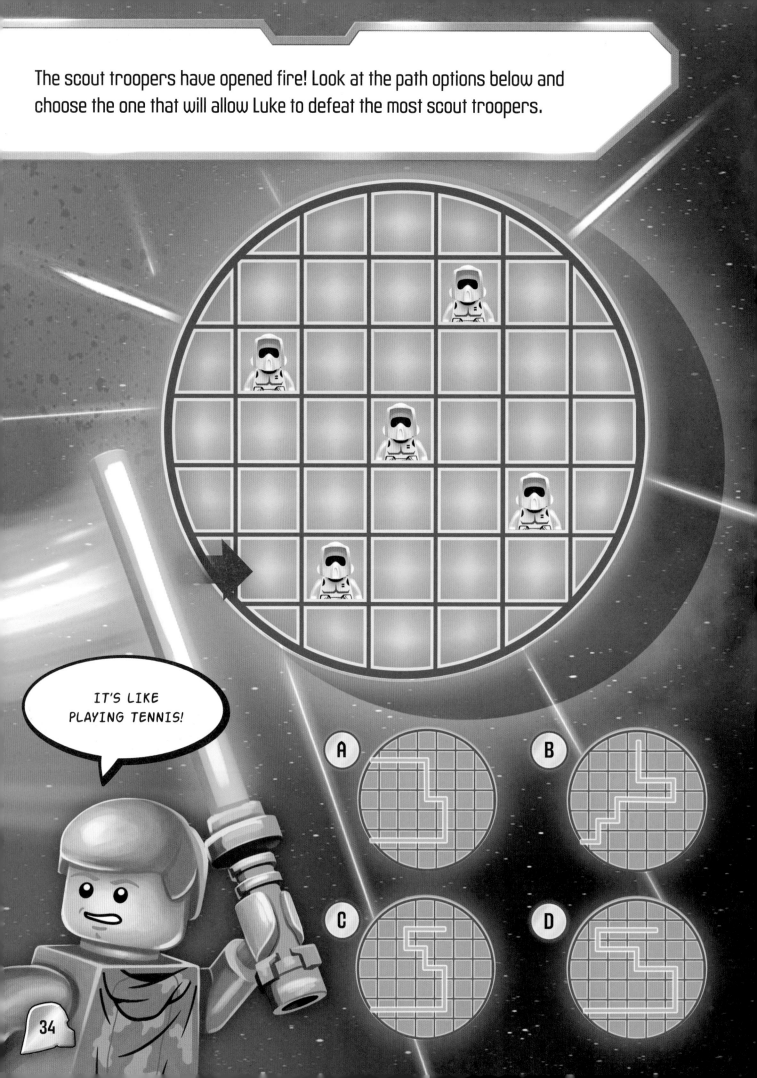

IT'S LIKE PLAYING TENNIS!

A

B

C

D

Circle the two parts on C-3PO's screen that do not belong to Luke's speeder bike.

How many differences can you find between these two scout troopers?

I CAN SPOT 9 DIFFERENCES. BUT, YOU KNOW, I'M A JEDI!

Complete Luke and Han's domino tiles by writing the correct numbers in the empty spaces. Each face should match the face on the tile next to it.

Which of these friends have been caught in an Ewok trap? Tick the circles underneath the characters you can see in the net.

GREAT, CHEWIE! GREAT! ALWAYS THINKING WITH YOUR STOMACH.

Learn how to draw an adorable Ewok with this step-by-step guide.
Part of the drawing has been done for you.

①

②

③

GOOD JOB, CHEWIE!

GRRRR!

FAST AND FURRY

ON THE FOREST MOON OF ENDOR, LUKE IS PREPARING FOR A SECRET MISSION TO DESTROY THE DREADFUL DEATH STAR ONCE AND FOR ALL ...

WE'RE SHORT ON PARTS, THREEPIO. WE NEED TO FIND VEHICLES TO SALVAGE.

THIS STOLEN IMPERIAL SPEEDER BIKE WILL BE VERY USEFUL FOR OUR MISSION.

ONE MORE BOLT, AND IT'S GOOD AS NEW!

WELL DONE, MASTER LUKE!

IT LOOKS LIKE THIS LITTLE EWOK WANTS TO HELP, TOO.

YUB NUB!

UMM ... NO, HE ONLY WANTS TO RIDE THIS BIKE.

NO PROBLEM. OUR FURRY ALLIES SHOULD KNOW HOW TO USE IMPERIAL TECH.

HERE, COME CLOSER, LITTLE FRIEND. I'LL TEACH YOU.

Luke and his friends are surrounded by furry Ewoks!
How many Ewoks can you count? Write the total in the white circle.

C-3PO is floating! Which of the shadows matches his?

PUT ME DOWN! HELP, MASTER LUKE!

A

B

C

Who is Vader's other child and Luke's twin? Find out by circling the sets of pictures in the grid and seeing which one is left. One has been found for you.

Luke has gone to meet his father. Find the path from Luke to Vader by going through the yellow colours in neighbouring hexagons.

Emperor Palpatine is always heavily guarded. Count how many Royal Guards you can see, and write the total in the empty circle below.

DON'T YOU LOVE THOSE AWESOME RED OUTFITS?

Oh, no! Palpatine's throne room is missing some pieces. Match the picture pieces to the big picture and write the correct letters in the empty spaces.

YOU'LL FIND THE PIECES ELECTRIFYING!

A   B   C   D   E

Which Imperial trooper should appear at the end of each sequence?
Write the correct letters in the empty spaces.

Draw straight lines between the matching symbols. The person who is crossed by all of the lines is the one Vader wanted to turn to the Dark Side along with Luke.

The Rebel Alliance's X-wing has come under attack! Guide it through the tricky maze without being hit by laser-fire.

START

FINISH

45

Which drawing is an exact copy of the image of Luke battling Darth Vader?

Write the letters of the jigsaw pieces in the correct spaces to complete this picture of Luke duelling with Vader.

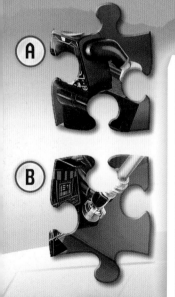

Help Lando and Nien Nunb and the *Millennium Falcon* escape the Imperial fighters by getting through this maze.

Look at the sequence of bricks in the box below. Which ship has the same sequence hidden in the row next to it?

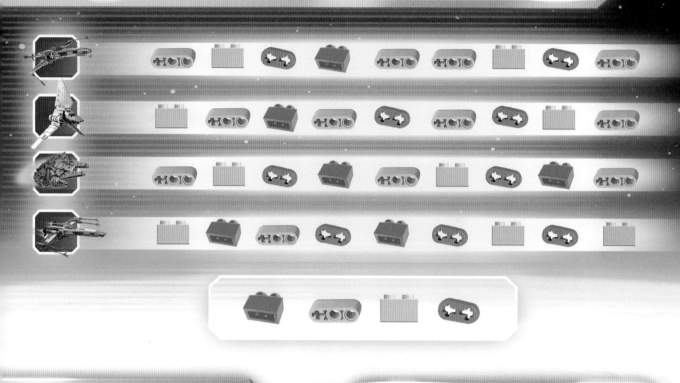

The second Death Star is exploding! Lead Luke to safety by drawing a line along his ship's trail without touching the sides or going off the edge.

Put a tick above the small picture pieces that appear in this explosive scene.

Write the correct letters above the picture jumble on the right to show how Chewbacca and the Ewoks stole an Imperial AT-ST Walker.

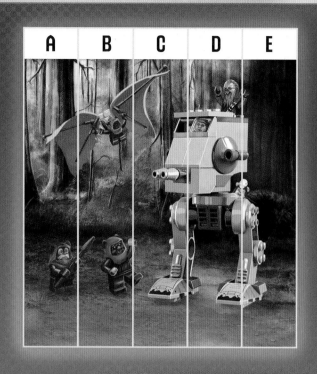

| A | B | C | D | E |

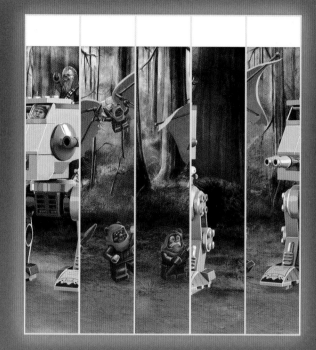

Use the grid to finish this picture of an AT-ST Walker.

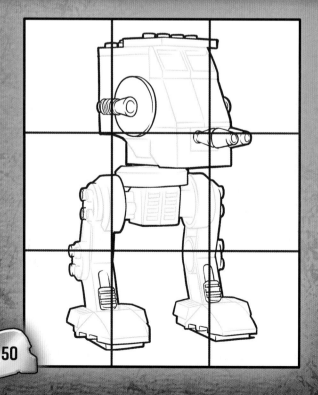

GREAT PILOT

THE REBELS' ATTACK ON THE SECOND DEATH STAR WAS A SURPRISING SUCCESS. HAVING DEFEATED DARTH VADER, LUKE SKYWALKER FLEW OFF THE IMPERIAL BATTLE STATION AT THE VERY LAST MOMENT ...

PHEW! THAT WAS CLOSE!

NOW, BACK TO ENDOR!

HEY! WHO ARE YOU?

DARTH VA— I MEAN ... ANAKIN SKYWALKER, YOUR FATHER.

WHAT? I SAW YOU A MINUTE AGO! YOU LOOKED DIFFERENT!

WELL, I'M A FORCE GHOST NOW ...

COOL STARSHIP. IS IT YOURS?

Draw straight lines between the Ewoks to mark where the rope should go to defeat the AT-ST. The lines can't go through obstacles.

Time to celebrate – Ewok-style! Find the sequence of three dancing Ewoks in each of the rows below.

Match the silhouette to one of the groups below to find out which three Force ghosts Luke has seen.

 A

 C

 B

 D

Hooray! The Rebellion has won! Look at Luke and his three friends in the box below and see if you can find them in the celebration.

COME ON, GUYS! IT'S TIME TO PARTY!

You've come to the end of your galactic adventure! Now test your knowledge of Luke Skywalker with this quiz.

1. LUKE SKYWALKER IS:

(A) A JEDI KNIGHT

(B) A ROYAL GUARD

(C) A STORMTROOPER

2. LUKE'S LIGHTSABER LOOKS LIKE:

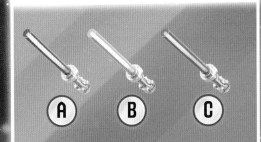

(A)   (B)   (C)

3. LUKE'S SPEEDER BIKE IS:

(A) RED AND YELLOW

(B) GREEN AND ORANGE

(C) BLACK AND BROWN

4. LUKE'S TWIN IS:

(A) LEIA ORGANA

(B) HAN SOLO

(C) LANDO CALRISSIAN

5. LUKE WAS TAUGHT BY THIS JEDI:

(A) OBI-WAN KENOBI

(B) YODA

(C) ANAKIN SKYWALKER

(D) OBI-WAN KENOBI AND YODA

ANSWERS

p. 6

D

p. 6

p. 7

p. 8

2 3 1

p. 9

C

p. 9

p. 10

D

Mind trick

p. 11

p. 12

C

p. 12

p. 13

1 2
3 5

p. 18

3
4 2 5 1

p. 18

5
2 3
1 4

p. 21

p. 20

8 3 2
1 4 5
6 7 9

p. 20

D

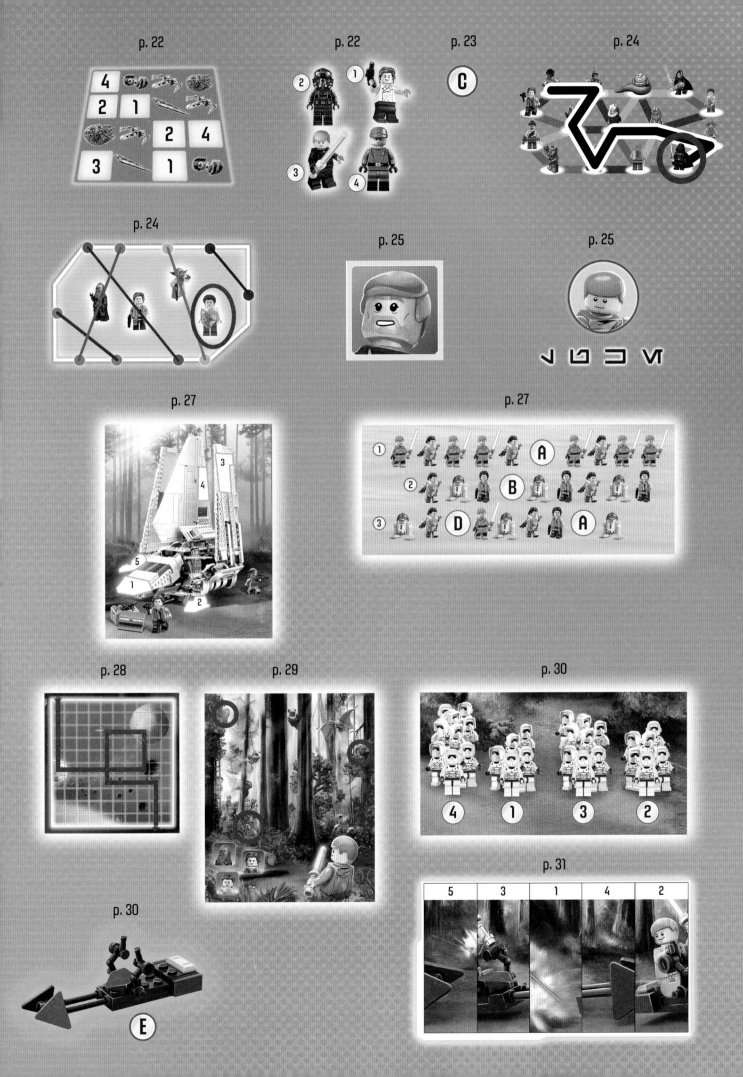

p. 22

p. 22

p. 23

p. 24

p. 24

p. 25

p. 25

p. 27

p. 27

p. 28

p. 29

p. 30

p. 30

p. 31

p. 32

p. 33

p. 33

p. 34

p. 35

p. 35

p. 36

p. 36

p. 40

p. 41

p. 42

p. 43

p. 44

p. 45

LEIA

14

C

D

A C D

A B

E

5 2 1

4 3 6

12

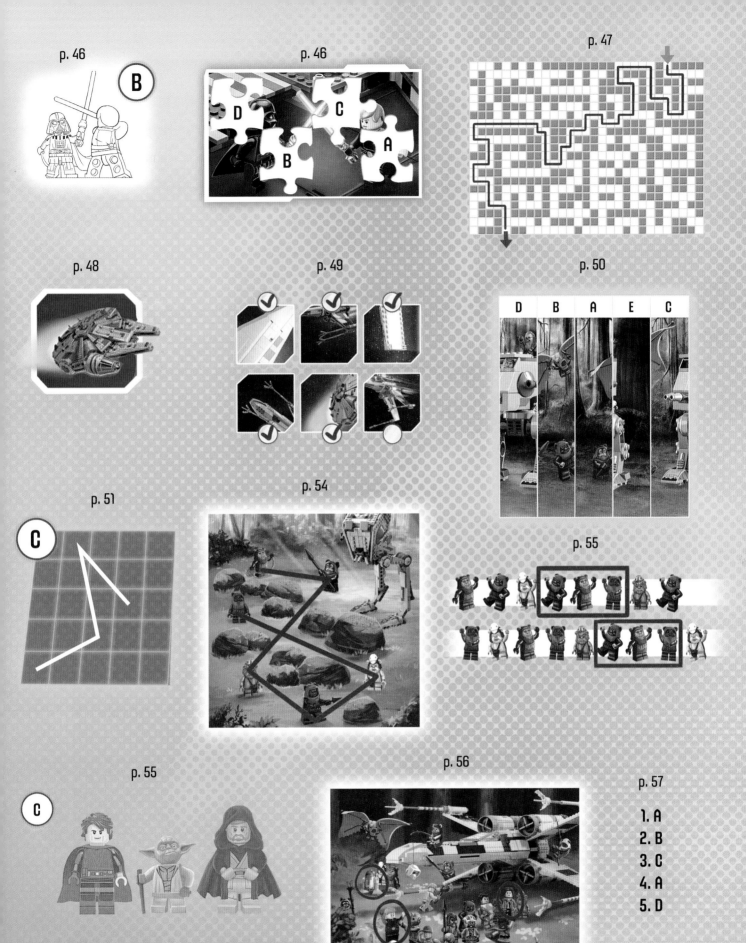

p. 46

p. 46

p. 47

p. 48

p. 49

p. 50

p. 51

p. 54

p. 55

p. 55

p. 56

p. 57

B

D C B A

D B A E C

C

C

1. A
2. B
3. C
4. A
5. D

How to build Luke Skywalker

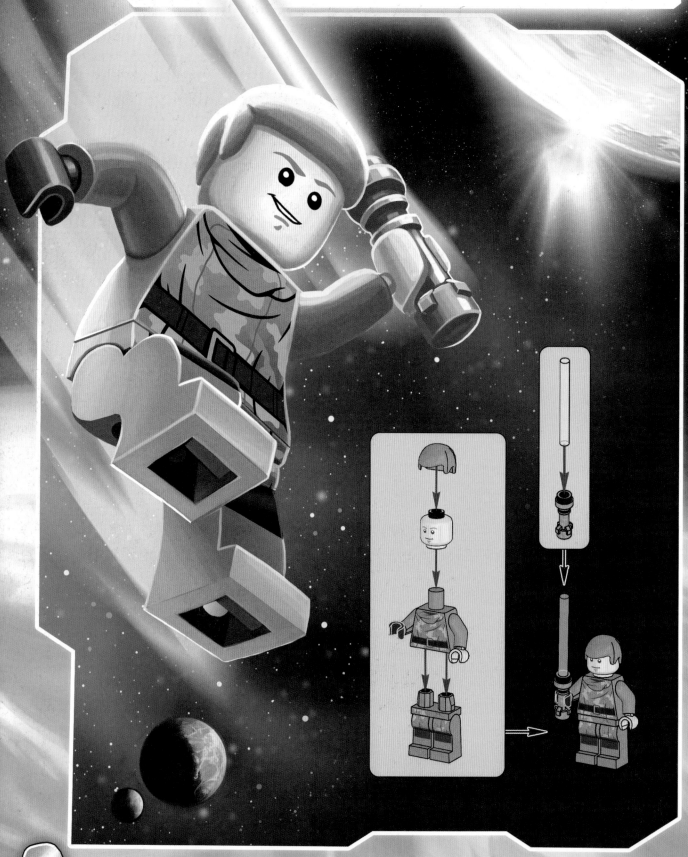